Popular TV Themes

Wise Publications
London/New York/Paris/Sydney/
Copenhagen/Madrid

Exclusive Distributors:
Music Sales Limited
8/9 Frith Street, London W1V 5TZ, England.
Music Sales Pty Limited
120 Rothschild Avenue, Rosebery, NSW 2018, Australia.

This book © Copyright 1997 by Wise Publications
Order No. AM936970
ISBN 0-7119-5745-2

Cover design by Hutton & Partners
Compiled by Peter Evans
Music arranged by Stephen Duro
Music processed by Allegro Reproductions

Cover photograph courtesy of
Rex Features

Your Guarantee of Quality:

As publishers, we strive to produce every book to the highest commercial standards.

The music has been freshly engraved and the book has been carefully designed to minimise awkward page turns
and to make playing from it a real pleasure.

Particular care has been given to specifying acid-free, neutral-sized paper made from pulps which have not been
elemental chlorine bleached. This pulp is from farmed sustainable forests and was produced with special regard
for the environment.

Throughout, the printing and binding have been planned to ensure a sturdy, attractive publication which should
give years of enjoyment.

If your copy fails to meet our high standards, please inform us and we will gladly replace it.

Music Sales' complete catalogue lists thousands of titles and is available in full colour sections by subject, direct
from Music Sales Limited. Please state your areas of interest and send a cheque/postal order for £1.50 for
postage to: Music Sales Limited, Newmarket Road, Bury St. Edmunds, Suffolk IP33 3YB.

Visit the Internet Music Shop at
http://www.musicsales.co.uk

Printed in the United Kingdom by
Halstan & Co Limited, Amersham, Buckinghamshire.

Force Field (Theme from 'The Crystal Maze') 4

Gladiators 9

Happy Days 14

Hi De Hi Holiday Rock (Theme from 'Hi De Hi') 17

I'm Always Here (Theme from 'Baywatch') 20

London's Burning 22

Madson 25

Neighbours 28

Nessun Dorma (from 'Turandot') (Theme from 'World Cup '90') 31

Psalm 23 (Theme from 'The Vicar Of Dibley') 34

Red Dwarf 38

Rumpole (Of The Bailey) 40

Star Trek 42

Telly Addicts 44

The Black Adder (Theme from) 6

Where Everybody Knows Your Name (Theme from 'Cheers') 46

Force Field
(Theme from 'The Crystal Maze')

By Zack Laurence

Theme From The Black Adder

Music by Howard Goodall

March tempo

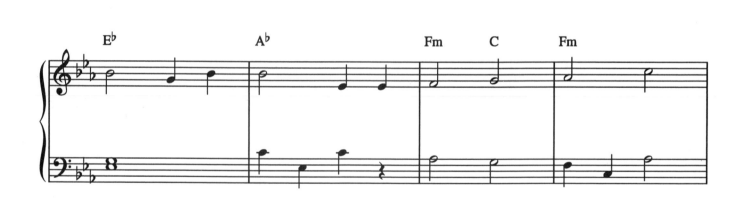

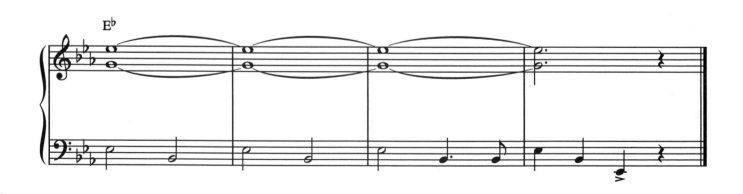

Gladiators

By Muff Murfin

Moderately

Faster

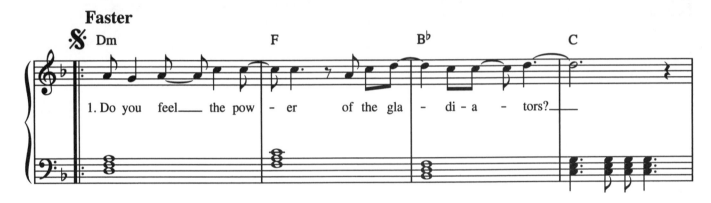

1. Do you feel— the pow - er of the gla - di - a - tors?—

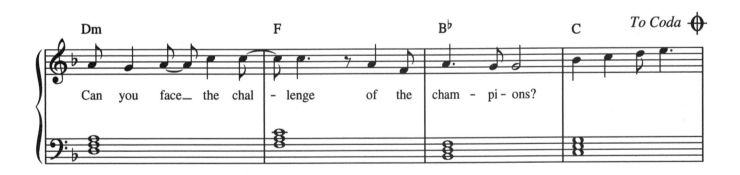

Can you face— the chal - lenge of the cham - pi - ons?

To Coda

Do you have— the cou - rage of a he - ro?

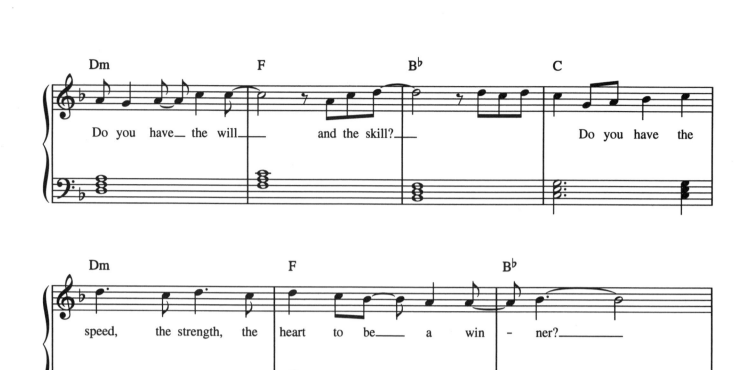

gotta breathe fire, a tiger; gotta give your

all to win;— ready or not, let the challenge begin.—

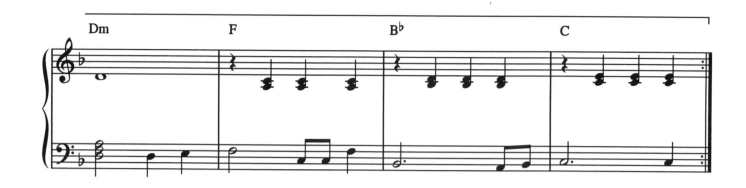

D.S. al Coda

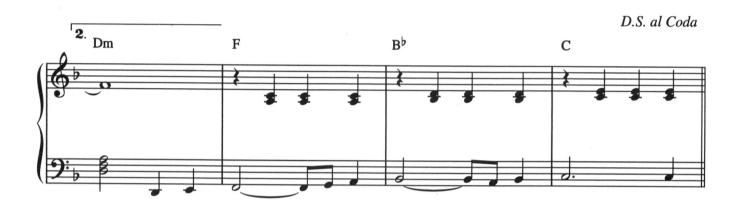

CODA

Show the stuff___ you're made___ of,___ can you seal___ the fate___

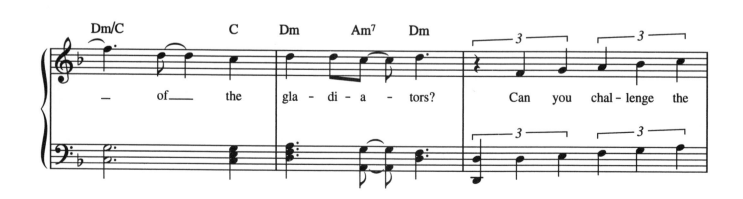

— of___ the gla - di - a - tors? Can you chal - lenge the

gla - di - a - tors?   Will you take on the   gla - di - a - tors?

Will you be the new   cham - pion?___

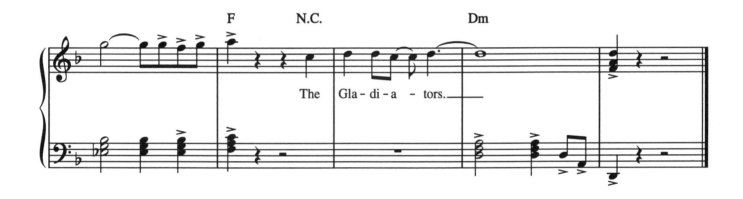

The Gla - di - a - tors.___

Verse 2:

Can you match the strength of the gladiators?
Do you have the fire within you?
Do you have the heart of a lion?
Do you have the power in your soul?
Now it's time to race, it's face to face
Get on the track now,
Your future's on the line.
Are you a gladiator?

Break:

Got to move at frightening speed,
Skill and strength are what you need,
Got to take it on the chin,
Got to love it, love to fight and win.

Happy Days

Music by Charles Fox
Words by Norman Gimbel

Hi De Hi Holiday Rock
(Theme from 'Hi De Hi')

Words & Music by Jimmy Perry

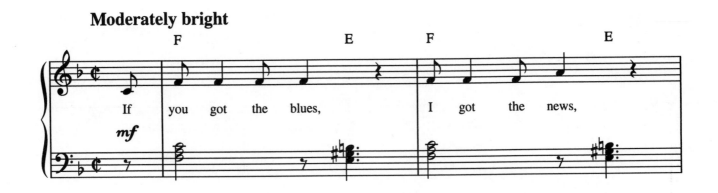

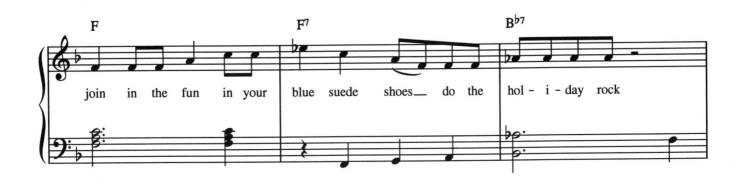

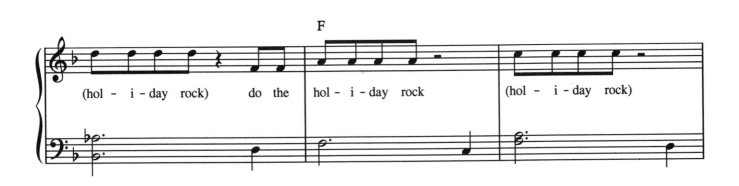

I'm Always Here
(Theme from 'Baywatch')

Words & Music by Cory Lerios, John D'Andrea, Joe Henry & Jimmy Jamison

London's Burning

By Simon Brint & Roddy Matthews

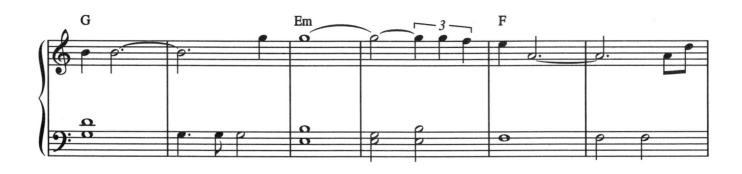

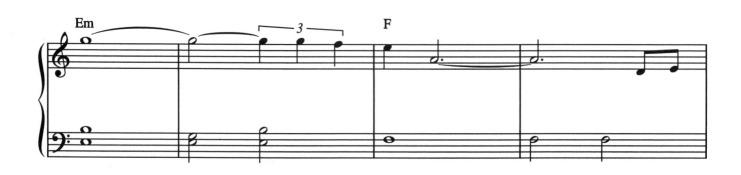

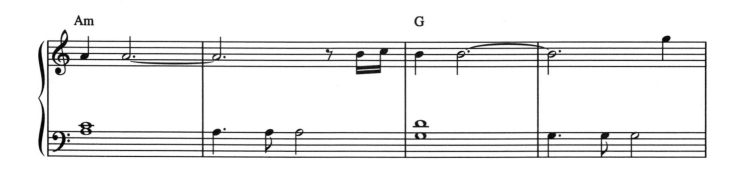

Madson

By Denis King

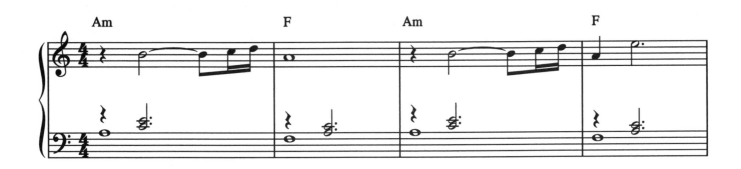

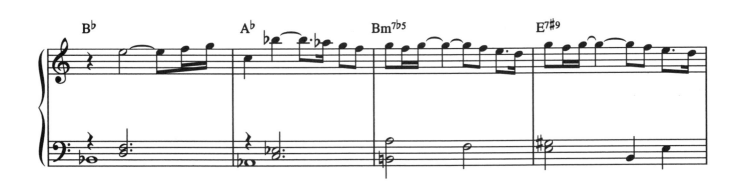

Neighbours

Words & Music by Tony Hatch & Jackie Trent

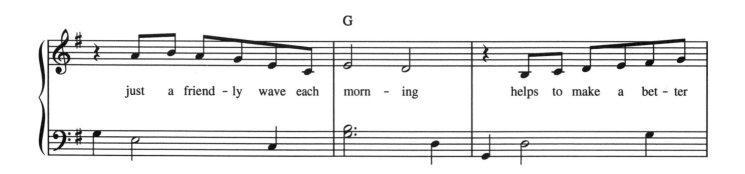

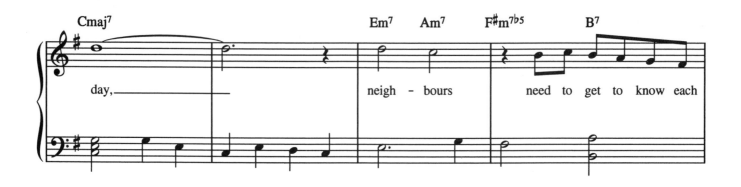

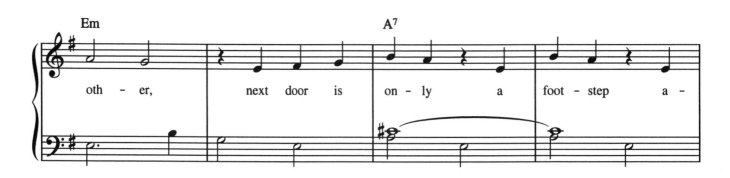

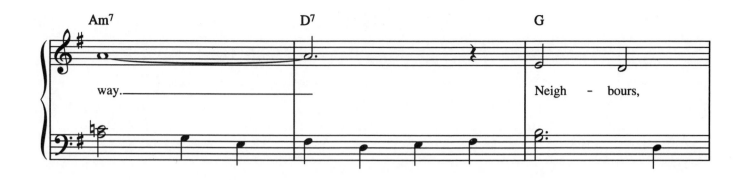

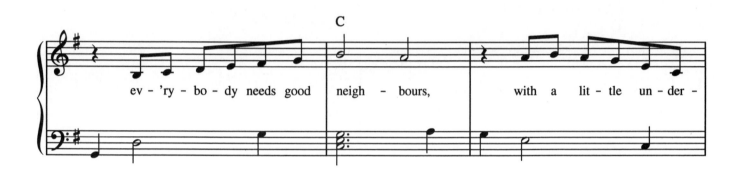

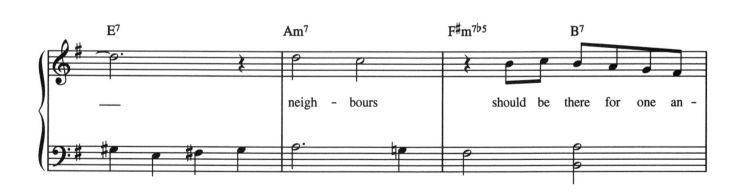

oth - er, that's when good neigh - bours be -

come good friends. That's when good neigh - bours be -

1. come good friends.

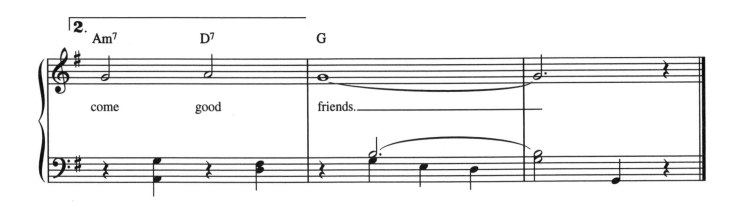

2. come good friends.

Nessun Dorma (From Turandot)

By Giacomo Puccini

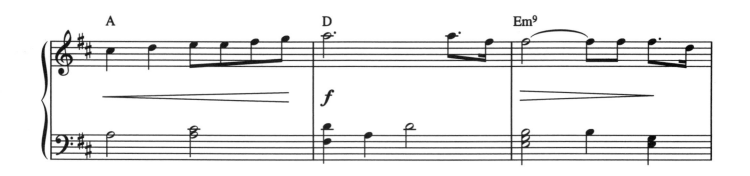

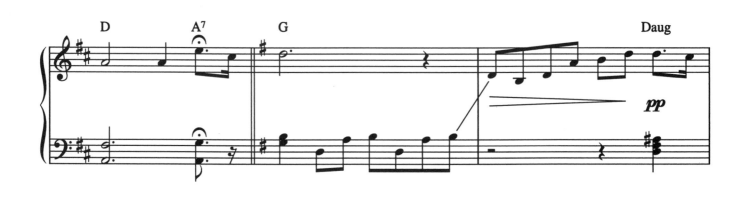

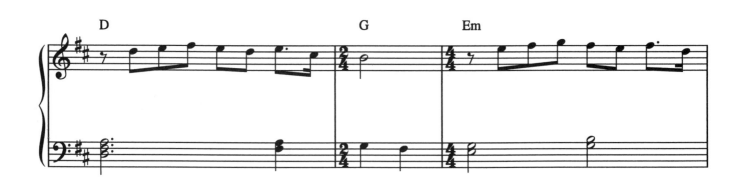

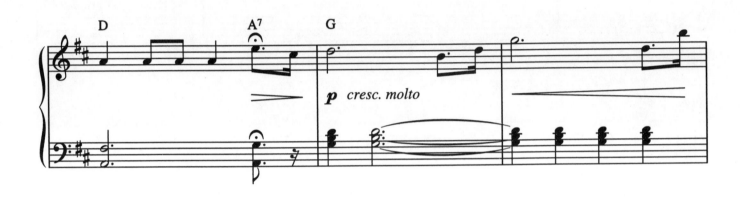

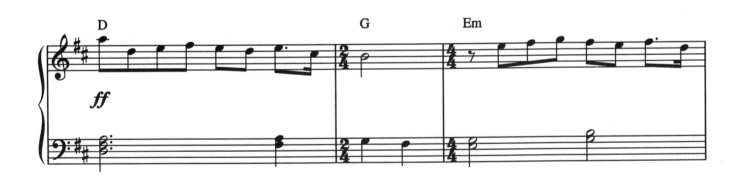

Psalm 23
(Theme From 'The Vicar Of Dibley')

By Howard Goodall

Moderately

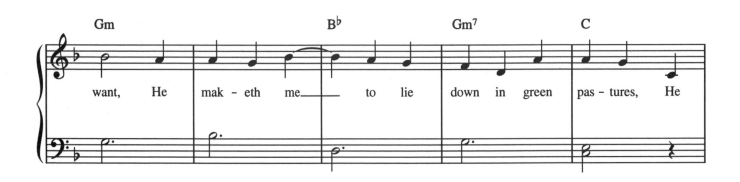

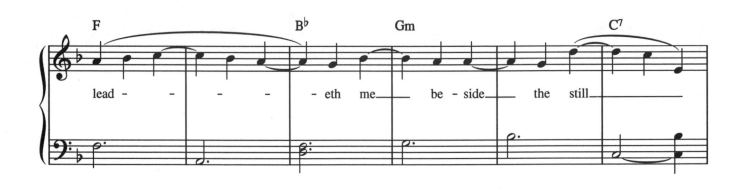

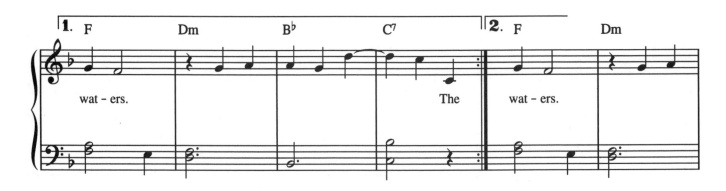

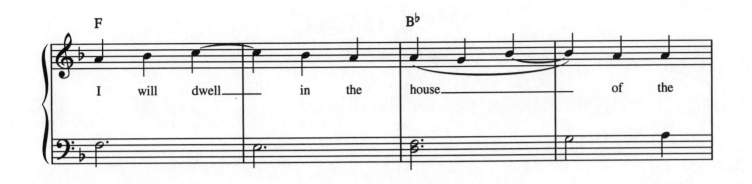

I will dwell__ in the house__ of the

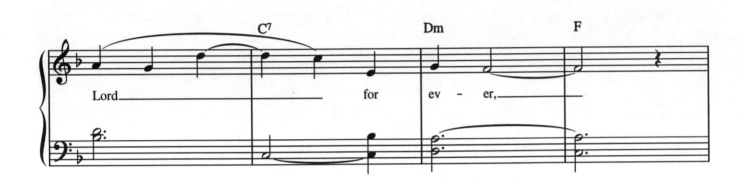

Lord__ for ev - er,__

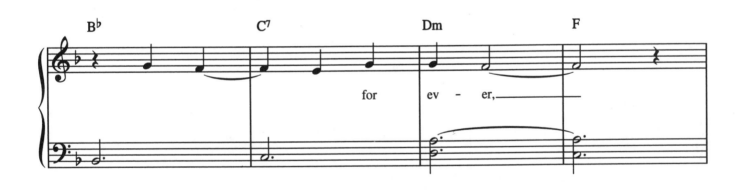

for ev - er,__

for ev - er.__

Red Dwarf

By Howard Goodall

Moderately

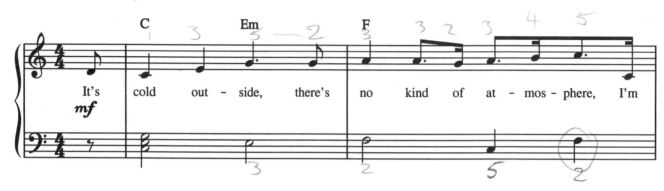

It's cold out - side, there's no kind of at - mos - phere, I'm

all a - lone, more or less,___ Let me fly

far a - way from here; Fun, fun, fun___ in the sun, sun,

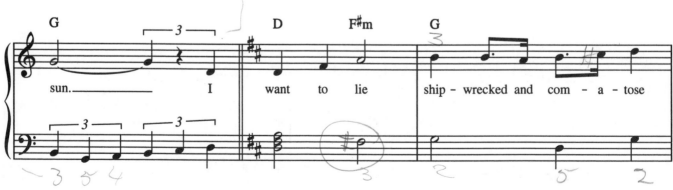

sun.___ I want to lie ship - wrecked and com - a - tose

Rumpole (Of The Bailey)

By Joseph Horovitz

Star Trek

By Alexander Courage

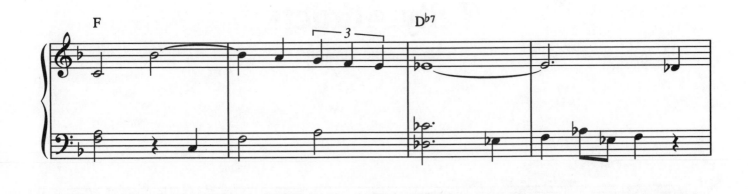

Telly Addicts

By George Fenton

Where Everybody Knows Your Name
(Theme from 'Cheers')

Music by Gary Portnoy
Words by Judy Hart Angelo

Moderately slow

Mak-ing your way in the world to-day takes ev-'ry thing you've got

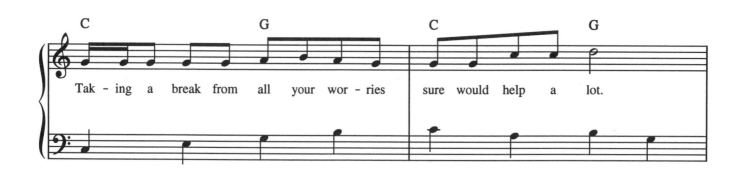

Tak-ing a break from all your wor-ries sure would help a lot.

Would-n't you like to get a-way? Some-times you want to

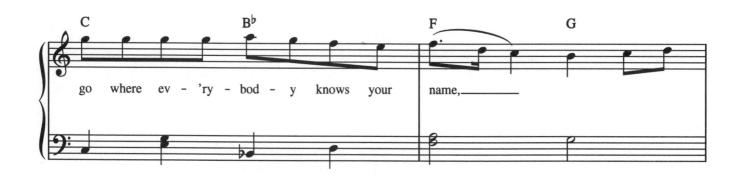

go where ev-'ry-bod-y knows your name,____

Simply, the easiest
books of popular music
for piano ever!